SUNDAY EXPRESS & DAILY EXPRESS
CARTOONS

Twenty-fifth Series

A DAILY EXPRESS PUBLICATION

Published by Beaverbrook Newspapers Limited, Fleet Street, London, E.C.4, and printed by Purnell and Sons, Ltd., Paulton (Somerset) and London

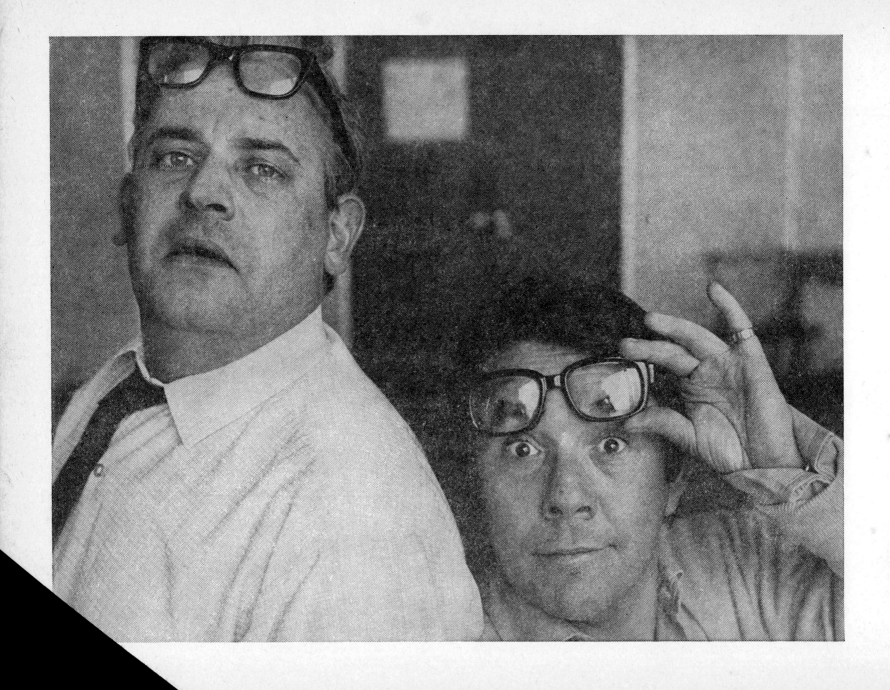

INTRODUCTION by The Two Ronnies

RONNIE BARKER: Look, we've been asked to write an introduction to Giles this year.

RONNIE CORBETT: Whatever for? Giles doesn't need any introduction, surely. Everybody knows Giles.

RONNIE BARKER: Yes, but this is to introduce his Cartoon Annual.

RONNIE CORBETT: Everybody knows that as well.

RONNIE BARKER: What would you say was his most admirable quality?

RONNIE CORBETT: He's funny. Very funny.

RONNIE BARKER: Oh, I know he's funny. But he has his serious side.

RONNIE CORBETT: True. But he's funny with it.

RONNIE BARKER: His drawing is terribly accurate.

RONNIE CORBETT: Yes—and very funny.

RONNIE BARKER: Would you say it was enough, just to be funny?

RONNIE CORBETT: More than enough. I mean, what's better than a good laugh?

RONNIE BARKER: Well——

RONNIE CORBETT: Apart from that. What's better than a bookful of grins and giggles? What can replace a basinful of fun? And who better to provide them than that master of the comic expression, that brilliant observer and portrayer of the much maligned human figure, that genius of the apt and the topical, the world-renowned Giles?

RONNIE BARKER: Thank you. You've just written it for me. I say, do you think the introduction should be funny?

RONNIE CORBETT: What, with a bookful of Giles to follow? That would be chancing your arm, wouldn't it?

"I'm not one of the hijackers, I'm keeping my wife covered in case she sings."

(During a recent hijacking a lady kept passengers "happy" by singing to them.)

Daily Express, September 8th, 1970

"How long the company is going to allow us to fly empty Jumbos backwards and forwards remains to be seen."

Daily Express, September 10th, 1970

"I'm not hijacking her—just a little trap to stop her nicking my marrows for this year's Harvest Festival."

Sunday Express, September 13th, 1970

"Frightful bore, actually. Not one hijacker the whole trip from Manchester to Heathrow."

Daily Express, September 15th, 1970

"I think you're as safe kissing Butch as you know who."

Daily Express,
September 17th, 1970

"Pity we can't hear what he's saying for sonic booms—I always love the Battle of Britain service."

Sunday Express, September 20th, 1970

"I am aware of Lord Goodman's opinion that the British Legal System is 'Demented', nevertheless this boy did willfully commit the serious crime of acquiring sixpennyworth of sweets after legal shopping hours."

Sunday Express, September 27th, 1970

"I ask you in the nicest possible way already—please do not sweep another load of haddock heads under my barrow."

Daily Express, September 29th, 1970

"Harry's good on the short sharp burst of four-letter words, but his missus can stay the distance longer."

Daily Express, October 1st, 1970

"Sounds good, don't it? 'My dearest Lucinda, Can't get away to marry you today as I'm cleaning out Battersea Sewage Station'."

Sunday Express, October 4th, 1970

"'Tis unfortunate, but according to our research on your ancestry you come out as Nixon's aunt."

Daily Express, October 6th, 1970

"Psst! Lady—want any anti-hijack pills, ten dollars a dozen?"

Daily Express, October 8th, 1970

"I hardly feel, dear, that because the sink at Balmoral hasn't been working properly since your great-great-grandmother's time, it justifies claiming a rent rebate."

Daily Express, November 5th, 1970

"Bertie couldn't stick his sergeant at Mafeking and he can't stick him leading the Armistice Parade today."

Sunday Express, November 8th, 1970

"Galloping into the last furlong, taking the bit between his teeth and sweating a bit at the hard going, comes the odds-on favourite streaking towards the winning post. And when you've passed it the General Manager would like a word with you in his office."

Daily Express, November 12th, 1970

"Harry, in asking you to appear in a TV commercial, 'Whiter than White' bears no reference to your spiritual aspirations—simply to your collar and surplice."

Sunday Express, November 15th, 1970

"The show must go on . . ."

Daily Express, November 19th, 1970

"I hope this is the last time Vera lets herself get talked into being the front half of a cow for a Young Liberals' demonstration."

Sunday Express, November 22nd, 1970

"One thing for sure, Buttercup—no one can accuse a cattle market of looking like a beauty contest."

Daily Express, November 24th, 1970

"I sometimes have doubts about some of ours, Mac. Grave doubts."

Daily Express, November 26th, 1970

"£2,310,000 for one painting is better odds than Littlewoods or horse racing."

(A painting was sold for this figure at Christies.)

Sunday Express, November 29th, 1970

"Do you know, young man, that Rolls-Royce and Courtaulds have banned this nude Safety Poster without your addition of a moustache and one or two other things?"

Daily Express, December 1st, 1970

" 'Come on, boyso,' he said, 'let's see if we can make a Henry Cooper out of you'."

Daily Express, December 3rd, 1970

"I should consider myself a very silly little bustard to make a comeback looking like a turkey just before Christmas."

Sunday Express, December 6th, 1970

"Right—if I give you my solemn promise not to short-change you, have I got your word you won't underpay *me*?"

Daily Express, December 8th, 1970

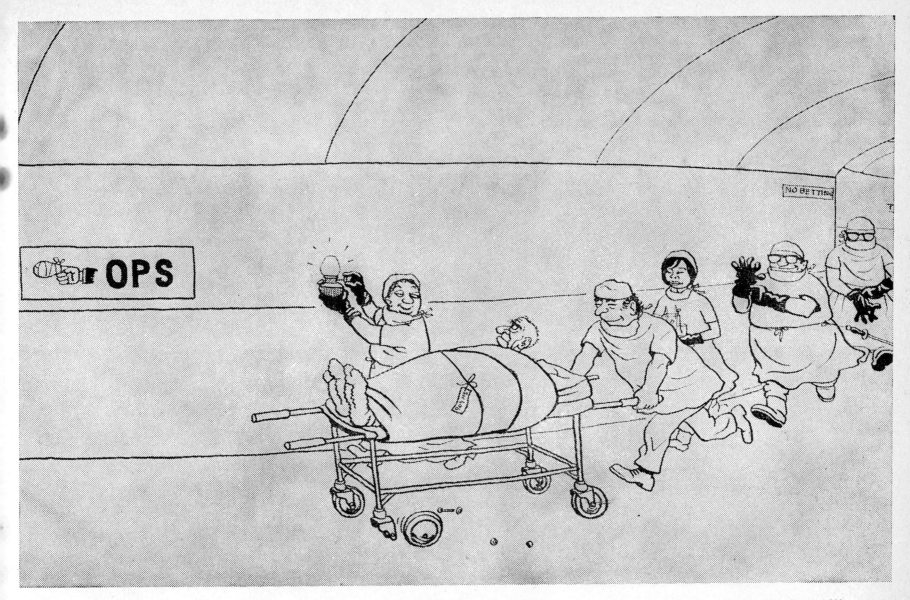

"Just in case of power-cuts, Mr. Wimple—we can't have Doctor whipping out all the wrong bits and pieces, can we?"

Daily Express, December 10th, 1970

"If you want to get on in the world I cannot emphasise too strongly the importance of attending the Daily Express Careers Exhibition."

Daily Express, December 12th, 1970

"Grandma! Did you lock this lady's husband somewhere when he came to read the electricity meter? Answer yes or no."

Sunday Express, December 13th, 1970

"The manager would like a word with you as to why the lift was stuck between two floors for one hour after the power cuts ended."

Daily Express, December 15th, 1970

"Now this merry festive death-ray gun, Madam, lets out a stream of devastating nerve gas which disintegrates any living object within range. And boy, do I wish it did!"

Daily Express, December 17th, 1970

"I told Vicar we intend to strike on Christmas Eve when it'll hurt most
and he said the way we have been singing lately it was a good idea."

Sunday Express, December 20th, 1970

"Go tell Father Christmas that Mummy Christmas has come to join the office party."

Daily Express, December 22nd, 1970

Sunday Express, December 27th, 1970

"We're parked on a double yellow line."

Daily Express, December 29th, 1970

"Pity you can't train that damn dog of yours to read a few population explosion warnings."

Daily Express, December 31st, 1970

"In view of his team being knocked out of the Cup yesterday, for goodness sake let him win."

Sunday Express, January 3rd, 1971

"Ahoy there, Mummy—The Press Gang's here to take you to the Boat Show."

Daily Express, January 5th, 1971

"Yet another indisputable advantage of Sail versus Power, sir—take the threat of an oil strike."

Daily Express, January 8th, 1971

"How you can sit there and expect me to cook your breakfast with poor Georgie Best thrown out in the cold by that wicked Matt Busby."

Sunday Express, January 10th, 1971

"They've sent me home because I'm wearing a trouser suit."

Daily Express, January 12th, 1971

"I know he didn't. But it's good for trade."

Daily Express, January 13th, 1971

"I wouldn't fancy our striking postmistress's chances of having her trespasses forgiven
if Vicar's pools don't reach their destination on time."

Sunday Express, January 17th, 1971

"I hope they don't stay out too long—you can lose the taste."

Daily Express, January 19th, 1971

"Dad says we don't want postmen, telephones, telegrams, or radio when Mrs. Yackharty's around."

Daily Express, January 21st, 1971

"Now I'd have been inclined to let her pay me pension before I called her a black legging old scab."

Sunday Express, January 24th, 1971

"Sure we're 24 hours behind everybody else—thanks to your freelance 'beat the strike' mail delivery service."

Daily Express, January 26th, 1971

"I've been arguing with that one for the last thirty years over £ s. d."

Sunday Express, January 31st, 1971

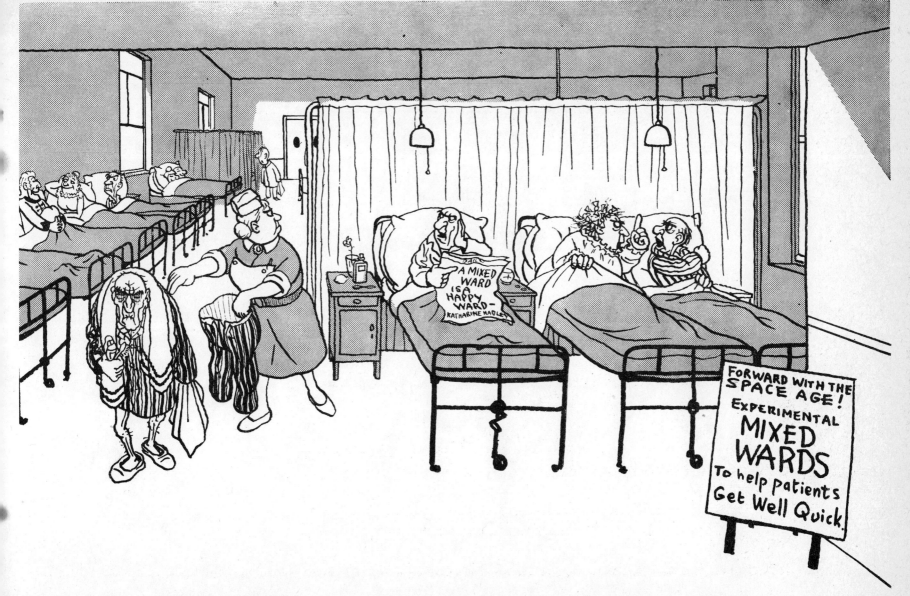

"Mixed wards aren't curing me very quick, with these two ding-donging next to me all day."

Daily Express, February 2nd, 1971

"You can certainly tell the ones who haven't won £250,000 this week."

("Laughing Bus Driver Wins £250,000"—headline.)

Daily Express, February 4th, 1971

"He says we owe $65.90 duty. You got $65.90, Ed?"

Sunday Express, February 7th, 1971

"According to her new decimal prices, the mints work out at 11s. 6d. each and 9d. extra for the holes."

Daily Express, February 9th, 1971

"As I don't like the idea of large sums of money lying around the house, any chance of a Securicor van and a couple of guard dogs?"

Daily Express, February 12th, 1971

"It was sweet of you, Ronnie, to deliver my Valentine to Reggie, and I'm sorry
a crowd of G.P.O. pickets saw you doing it."

Sunday Express, February 14th, 1971

"Shut up before you start! Thanks to decimal chit-chat I'm not half way through yesterday's round."

Daily Express, February 16th, 1971

"Art thou trying to start another War of t'bloody Roses, Mr. Walker?
Your new Yorkshire-Lancashire boundary goes right through my parlour."

Daily Express, February 18th, 1971

"Why do I have reason to suspect it is not the Queen? Because
the Queen would not use an expression like 'Shove off'."

(The Queen had been asked for proof of her identity by a police officer this week.)

Sunday Express, February 21st, 1971

"I don't think the Chief Constable should have fined them—he should have had it put in the Guinness Book of Records."

Daily Express, February 23rd, 1971

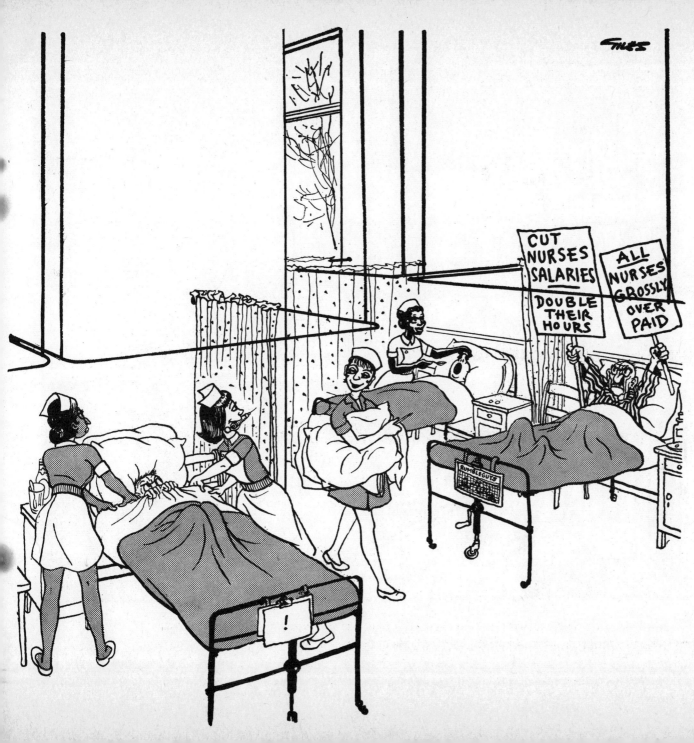

"He's a bit niggly because I confiscated a bottle of Scotch he'd smuggled under the sheets."

Daily Express, February 25th, 1971

"Don't you call me that—all I said was if the Ford strikers played the Leyland strikers charity football tomorrow, proceeds to go to the Post Office strikers, there'd be some sense in it."

Sunday Express, February 28th, 1971

"Switching on a milking machine don't make you an engineer and it didn't entitle you to take yesterday off in sympathy with the A.E.U."

Daily Express, March 2nd, 1971

"Boy! I'm glad I'm not editor of the 'Dear Sir' column when the post strike ends."

Daily Express, March 4th, 1971

"They say he's going to live in the R.A.F. under exactly the same conditions as the rest of us. Like hell he is."

Sunday Express, March 7th, 1971

"Let's just say that two letters in one whole day is because you're a little rusty, Miss Jones—not because you're trying to ease the load on the G.P.O."

Daily Express, March 9th, 1971

"Methinks someone has put a shot in our rear guard, inspector."

Daily Express, March 11th, 1971

"If you sell *your* free Cup tickets it won't be the F.A. you'll have to worry about—
it'll be your Auntie Rose and Uncle Bert."

Sunday Express, March 14th, 1971

"You can take that down—Thanks to Clay and Frazier, Vicar's talk on the love life of the Laughing Kookaburra Bird had a very poor attendance last Tuesday."

Daily Express, March 16th, 1971

"Blast the ruddy newspaper headlines."

Daily Express, March 20th, 1971

"Damn flowers—never a bottle of Scotch."

Sunday Express, March 21st, 1971

"I'm not holding up the bank, officer, I'm rounding up a few new customers."

Daily Express, March 23rd, 1971

"8–1 Friendly Way, and 5–4 Raquel Welch here ain't in the first three of the Belle of the Bar contest."

Daily Express, March 25th, 1971

"Grandma, my money box was right there on the mantelpiece before I went to spend a penny."

Sunday Express, March 28th, 1971

"Great idea of yours—let him have a bottle of Coke to celebrate his becoming a tax benefit."

Daily Express, April 1st, 1971

"I don't think Mr. Jones thought much of that tip Dad gave him for the National."

Sunday Express, April 4th, 1971

"Hang on, Sir—it won't take me an hour or so to check the rules."

Daily Express, April 6th, 1971

"Come on, Sir—admit you hate me."

Daily Express, April 8th, 1971

"May I have a show of hands for all those in favour of Princess Anne's comments on hot pants."

(Princess Anne had made some caustic comments on the new hot pants fashion.)

Sunday Express, April 11th, 1971

"What d'you mean—MISSED."

(A balloon force-landed and cut farmers' electricity supply this week.)

Daily Express, April 13th, 1971

"Looks like you've lost a couple of your short-back-and-sides, Horrie."

Daily Express, April 15th, 1971

"Well, thank you very much, that sure takes care of your Grandma's record—now how about your Father?"

Sunday Express, April 18th, 1971

"The question is, Miss Blewett: was it really wise to set your class an essay on 'My Favourite Film'?"

(A lady school teacher appeared in a much discussed sex educational film.)

Daily Express, April 20th, 1971

"Would you be interested in a comfortable night ashore in Co. Cork, sir? We'll keep an eye on your ship."

(Two Royal Navy ships were kidnapped by the I.R.A. this week.)

Daily Express, April 22nd, 1971

"They can feed me as many sex-educational films as they like—no one's going to convince me that our relatives had anything to do with sex."

Sunday Express, April 25th, 1971

"I said to my wife, 'Florrie, old dear, why don't you go in for it?' Then I said, 'No, old darling, you're too busy'."

Daily Express, April 27th, 1971

"That'll have to come down Your Grace. The Queen, Princess Anne, Margaret and the Queen Mother—Hot-pants, every man-jack of 'em."

Daily Express, April 29th, 1971

"I distinctly saw a disbelieving frown when the Umpire ruled 'Not out'."

Sunday Express, May 2nd, 1971

"I wondered if you've got any ideas before my husband finds out that Horace here has eaten his Cup Final ticket."

Daily Express, May 4th, 1971

"What a pity. It'll mean your cousin Henrietta won't be able to bring back any more little souvenir Spanish bulls."

Daily Express, May 6th, 1971

"I'm going to let mine run once more through the second half then I'm going to thump him."

Sunday Express, May 9th, 1971

"You'll never believe it, but she's never seen a sex-education film in her life."

Daily Express, May 11th, 1971

"I'm all for hot pants—by the time you've got 'em all back on again it's time for them to go home."

Daily Express, May 13th, 1971

"Women jockeys! Won't race in my colours unless I find her a matching lipstick."

"I told little miss next-door it was wind but I don't think she was very convinced."

Daily Express, May 20th, 1971

"Good try, Son—but I don't think the ladies of East Street Market are quite ready for your immaculate Common Market French."

Sunday Express, May 23rd, 1971

"This may be all right for Rue de la Pompidou but it ain't for Dock Road Dwellings."

Daily Express, May 25th, 1971

"Over 21!"

Daily Express, May 27th, 1971

"This anonymous note saying you have a bomb on board—we have reason to
believe it was sent by your wife who isn't very keen on sailing."

Sunday Express, May 30th, 1971

"Well, that was Whitsun—now shall we all try to get a little work done before Derby Day?"

Daily Express, June 1st, 1971

"Monsieur complains that your Aberdeen Angus has been striking up a kind of relationship with his champion Charolais."

Daily Express, June 3rd, 1971

"I am aware that a certain magistrate approves of four letter words in our Permissive Society, but I will not have them used in my Parish when referring to the weather, Mr. Matheson."

Sunday Express, June 6th, 1971

"Never did trust that Pig—'Come into the office and we'll negotiate,' he said."

Daily Express, June 8th, 1971

"This is Daddy—Daddy is flying with the Red Arrows this weekend."

Daily Express, June 12th, 1971

'Either you chuck in your job as weather forecaster or next year you go on holiday on your own.''

Sunday Express, June 13th, 1971

"Last chance, brother—straight down the line without a flinch or you're scratched for Ascot."

Daily Express, June 15th, 1971

"Watcha, Bertie—considering there is only one policeman for every 500 people in Britain you're a very lucky man. I am about to give you my undivided attention."

Daily Express, June 17th, 1971

"Who's been having a go at the bottle of whisky we bought Dad for Father's Day?"

Sunday Express, June 20th, 1971

"Ladies! Let's keep our Women's Lib. activities off the Centre Court."

Daily Express, June 22nd, 1971

"Someone has blundered—he got his call-up papers for the West German Home Guard this morning."

Daily Express, June 25th, 1971

"D'Arcy—if you must throw professional tantrums <u>do</u> try to keep your bat in the garden."

Sunday Express, June 27th, 1971

"Five past two! This is a raid."

Daily Express, June 29th, 1971

"Bad enough being rationed to one dog biscuit each without having HIM keep grumbling about the increased cost of living."

Daily Express, July 1st, 1971

"When I signed on for this job it didn't say anything about baby-sitting."

Sunday Express, July 4th, 1971

"Thanks to Bonnie Prince Charles opening a match on a horse, it looks as if we are in for some brighter cricket."

Daily Express, July 6th, 1971

"Ah, well, if they won't let us have a motor bike till we're seventeen, there's always the sea."

Daily Express, July 8th, 1971

"Which goes to prove that even if you don't think they're all little Florence Nightingales don't let them hear you say so."

Sunday Express, July 11th, 1971

"While you're writing to the Express about 'You and your lovable pet'. . ."

Daily Express, July 13th, 1971

"Surely it's not too much to ask you to amuse them for a few minutes before you go to work—I've got them all day."

Daily Express, July 22nd, 1971

"Harry always takes an hour or so to make absolutely sure they're bathing in the nude before he reports them to the police."

Sunday Express, July 25th, 1971

"This is another thing Happy Package Hols didn't include in their brochure."

Daily Express, July 29th, 1971

"Our landlady on the Costa Brava last year didn't clap you in irons just because you've got oily feet."

Sunday Express, August 1st, 1971

"Ahoy there, dear—are you ready? The Britannia's arrived—wind North to North-East—
only light showers, lovely day for a spinnaker run."

Daily Express, August 3rd, 1971

"As an M.P. determined to emulate his leader I can't help wishing you'd bought an organ."

Daily Express, August 10th, 1971

"Nixon's U.S.-on-the-rocks speech sure helped our overseas economy. Honey, that's the third Guide who's tipped me this morning."

Daily Express, August 17th, 1971

"I want to phone my lawyers
—he pulled my 'air."

Daily Express, August 26th, 1971

"But it *is* your scene, darling—and it will be all the other little boys' scene when you get back to school."

Daily Express, August 31st, 1971

"I think it's a lovely name for a boy. But I still can't see why they have to christen it on the day of our last match of the season."

Sunday Express, September 5th, 1971